Grammar
PRACTICE BOOK

Mc Graw Hill **Macmillan/McGraw-Hill**

The McGraw·Hill Companies

 Macmillan/McGraw-Hill

Published by Macmillan/McGraw-Hill, of McGraw-Hill Education, a division of The McGraw-Hill Companies, Inc.,
Two Penn Plaza, New York, New York 10121.

Printed in the United States of America

6 7 8 9 10 HES 13 12 11

Contents

Unit 2 • Our Families, Our Neighbors

Unit 3 • Have Fun!

Unit 4 • Let's Team Up

Unit 5 • Nature Watch

Unit 6 • Adventures

Name _____

A sentence is a group of words that tells a whole idea. A sentence begins with a capital letter.

Example: The cat can jump.

Circle the sentences.

1. She sat down.

2. We can jump up.

3. ran here.

4. Pat can do this.

5. we like to.

6. Pat and Nan

7. We ran and ran.

Name _____

A sentence is a group of words that tells a whole idea. A sentence begins with a capital letter.

Use the words in the box to make sentences.

| Pam | can jump | ran down | The bat |

_____

1. My cat _____.

2. _____ is little.

3. Sam _____.

4. Sam and _____ can jump.

Add and change words to make this a sentence.

5. sam can _____

_____

© Macmillan/McGraw-Hill

Name _____

Every sentence begins
with a capital letter.

Write each sentence correctly.

1. this is my cap.

_____

- -

2. you can go with me.

_____

- -

3. she sat down.

_____

- -

4. nan ran up.

_____

- -

5. he has the mat.

_____

- -

_____

Name _____

A sentence is a group of words that tells a whole idea.

Every sentence begins with a capital letter.

Write each sentence correctly.

1. we can nap here.

_____

_____

2. she ran and ran.

_____

_____

3. sam said to go up.

_____

_____

4. do not jump.

_____

_____

Add and change words to make this a sentence.

5. nan has

_____

_____

Name _____

Fill in the circle next to the complete sentence.

1. ○ Pam has to go.

   ○ not up here

   ○ has a hat.

2. ○ Pat and Sam

   ○ We jump down.

   ○ is with you

3. ○ Nan ran to me.

   ○ up and down the mat

   ○ is fat.

4. ○ a little pat for the cat

   ○ ran and ran

   ○ The cats can go up.

Write two of your own sentences.
Leave a space between words and between sentences.

_____

5. _____

_____

Name _____

The words in a sentence have to be in the right order.

The order has to make sense.

Correct: Sam ran over my cap.

Not correct: ran cap Sam my over.

Circle the sentences that have the words in the right order.

1. Dan jumps over the hat.

2. it We over jump.

3. Pat tags Dan.

4. She plays tag, too.

5. ran Sam here back.

Write your own sentence.
Check that all your letters and words are in order left to right.

_____

- -

_____

Name_____

The words in a sentence have to be in the right order.

The order has to make sense.

A sentence ends with a period.

Write the words in order. Write the period at the end.

1. looks Mack up.

_____

_____

2. my has bag He.

_____

_____

3. jump to said Pat.

_____

_____

4. bag over He the jumps.

_____

_____

5. it, We too do.

_____

_____

© Macmillan/McGraw-Hill

Name_____

> Every sentence ends with a special mark.
>
> Example: The man ran back.

Put a period at the end of each sentence.

Circle the mark.

1. Look at me go _____

2. Mack ran like this _____

3. She jumps over it _____

4. Hal is over there _____

5. We can play here _____

6. This is what I like to do _____

Name _____

The words in a sentence must make sense.

A sentence ends with a period.

Look at the sentences. Write C if a sentence is correct.
Fix the others by writing the words in order.
Write the period at the end.

1. not Pam can go. _____

_ _

_____

2. He has the map. _____

_ _

_____

3. The cat sat on it. _____

_ _

_____

4. down jumps She up and. _____

_ _

_____

5. Sam can see Hal. _____

_ _

_____

Name _____

Put an X next to sentences with the words out of order.

Put the words in order. Write the sentences correctly on the lines.

Check that each sentence ends with a period.

I. my is cat. Mack

_____

- -

_____

2. over the mat. jumps He

_____

- -

_____

3. Sam has a bag for Mack.

_____

- -

_____

4. Mack likes to play with it.

_____

- -

_____

5. too. He Sam, likes

_____

- -

_____

Name _____

A statement tells something.

A statement begins with a capital letter and ends with a period.

Example: Wag is little.

Draw a line under the statements.

1. Wag naps and naps.

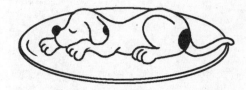

2. Digs too

3. Wag has my cap.

4. He runs to me.

5. sam rides

6. Wag and I play.

Name _____

A statement tells something.

A statement begins with
a capital letter and
ends with a period.

Example: Jan can ride.

Draw a line from the statement to its picture.

1. Jack can kick.

2. Pam runs.

3. The hat is too big.

4. Val has the bat.

Name _____

A statement begins with a capital letter.
A statement ends with a period.

Write each statement correctly.

1. Jack is quick _____

_ _

_____

2. he rides up and down _____

_ _

_____

3. Pam packs the bag _____

_ _

_____

4. she can do it _____

_ _

_____

5. we are big _____

_ _

_____

Name_____

A statement is a sentence that tells something.
A statement begins with a capital letter and ends
with a period.

Read each pair of statements.

Circle the statement that is correct.

I. She runs and jumps.

we jump, too

2. he sits down

Jack rides with me.

3. My cap is in here.

Pam can not see it

4. Sam can play this.

you can do it

Name _____

Draw a line under the statements.

1. In the bag
   He packs up.
   mack looks

2. This, too
   In here
   She said yes.

3. A big hat
   The hat fits me.
   Sees it

4. We can ride.
   Jumps over
   hal and Rick run.

5. Will be
   Kicks and runs
   Rick wins.

A question is a sentence that asks something.

A question ends with
a question mark.

Example: Where is that cat?

A. Write Q next to each question. Do not write anything if the sentence is not a question.

1. Is the cat there? _____

2. The cat is not here. _____

3. Did the cat go up? _____

4. Did the cat come down? _____

5. I did not see that cat. _____

6. Where can it be? _____

B. Write a question. Write a question mark at the end.

_____

_____

© Macmillan/McGraw-Hill

Name _____

An exclamation is a sentence that shows strong feelings.

An exclamation ends with an exclamation mark.

Example: What a fat cat that is!

Circle the exclamations.

1. Come here, quick!

2. What is it?

3. Look at that!

4. What a good cat you are!

5. Where did the little cat go?

6. Grab the cat!

Name _____

A question ends with a question mark.

Example: Can Pal do a trick?

An exclamation ends with an exclamation mark.

Example: That was a good trick!

Circle the correct end mark for each sentence.

Write the mark on the line.

1. Look out for Pal _____   ?   !

2. Grab him _____   ?   !

3. Will he jump on me _____   ?   !

4. He is too quick _____   ?   !

5. What can we do _____   ?   !

6. Can we trick Pal _____   ?   !

Name _____

A question asks something.
A question ends with a question mark.

An exclamation shows strong feelings.
An exclamation ends with an exclamation mark.

Write each sentence correctly. Write <u>C</u> if a sentence is correct.

I. Is it on the mat!

_____

- -

_____

2. That is big!

_____

- -

_____

3. Grab the cat quick?

_____

- -

_____

4. Can we come in!

_____

- -

_____

5. Is this a trap?

_____

- -

_____

Name _____

Put a question mark or an exclamation mark at the end of each sentence.

1. Come here, quick _____

2. What is that in the grass _____

3. Look at it jump up _____

4. Will it jump on me _____

5. Grab my hat _____

6. Run, run, run _____

7. Do you see it _____

8. Where did it go _____

Name _____

A sentence is a group of words that tells a whole idea. Every sentence begins with a capital letter and ends with a special mark.

Write each sentence correctly.
Begin with a capital letter.
Add the end mark shown in ( ).

1. she can use my help (period)

_____

_____

2. where did it land (question mark)

_____

_____

3. look at it go up (exclamation mark)

_____

_____

4. the wind will help now (period)

_____

_____

Name _____

Every sentence begins with a capital letter. Every sentence ends with a special mark.

Circle the sentence that is correct in each group.

1. hank runs fast

Hank runs fast

Hank runs fast.

2. can we help him win

Can we help him win?

can we help him win?

3. He wins!

he wins

He wins

Write a sentence that tells what can happen next. Use the correct mark at the end.

_____

- -

_____

Name _____

Begin every sentence with a capital letter.
End every sentence with a special mark.

Unscramble the words in the box to complete the sentence. Write the sentence correctly. Use the correct mark at the end.

1. we | sand can this use

_____

- -

2. will | it help do you me

_____

- -

3. look | crab that very little at

- -

_____

4. where | the go crab did

_____

- -

Name _____

Write C if a sentence is correct. If a sentence is not correct, write the letter or letters to tell how you would make it right.

Ⓐ   Begin with a capital letter.

Ⓑ   Put a special mark at the end.

Ⓒ   Do not change.

1. rick jumps on the mat.   _____

2. Will Pam run fast   _____

3. she can go like the wind   _____

4. Now Sam runs and jumps.   _____

5. did he land in the sand?   _____

6. That was a very good jump!   _____

Go back to the sentences. Circle any letter that should be capital. Put the correct mark at the end.

Name _____

Read the sentences. Write them correctly.

> will you help, too
> can you pick up bricks
> here are the bricks, Dad
> what a big help you are
> we like to help you

Write two statements from the box.

1. _____

2. _____

Write two questions from the box.

3. _____

4. _____

Write one exclamation from the box.

5. _____

Name _____

A noun is a word that names a person, a place, or a thing.

Say the name of the noun in the picture.

person   place   thing

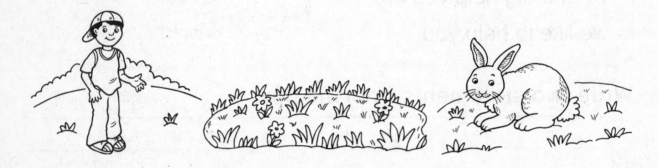

Circle the noun in each sentence.

1. Look at the little dog.

2. It sits in the grass.

3. The mom runs over.

4. They see an ant.

5. It digs up sand.

6. What a big hill that is!

Think of three more nouns. Say them to a partner.

Name _____

A noun is a word that names a person, place, or thing.

Write the noun from the word box to complete each sentence. Circle all the nouns in each sentence.

pond   pad   dad   rock   frog

_____

1. The little _____ jumps on the log.

2. The mom is in the _____.

3. Is that big fat frog the _____?

4. The dad sits on a _____.

5. They jump on the _____.

Name _____

A sentence begins with a capital letter.

A statement ends with a period.

Example: The cat sat in the hat.

Read each pair of sentences.
Circle the statement that is correct.

1. the mom is with her kit

   The mom is with her kit.

2. A kit is a little fox?

   A kit is a little fox.

3. Mom helps the little fox.

   Mom helps the little fox

4. now they play in the grass.

   Now they play in the grass.

> A noun names a person, place, or thing.
>
> Most sentences contain nouns.
>
> Begin every sentence with a capital letter.
>
> End every statement with a period.

Write the statement correctly. Circle the nouns.

1. i see one little cat

_____

_____

2. it can not go over the log

_____

_____

3. a cat does not jump like a frog

_____

_____

4. the mom will help

_____

_____

Talk with a partner. Think of five other nouns and say them aloud.

Name _____

Look at the underlined words in each sentence.
Write the one that is a noun.

1. I <u>am</u> a quick <u>little</u> <u>pig</u>. _____

2. Look at me <u>run</u> <u>down</u> the <u>hill</u>. _____

3. My <u>mom</u> <u>said</u> <u>to</u> come back. _____

4. <u>Help</u> your <u>dad</u> <u>now</u>. _____

5. I can lift <u>this</u> <u>big</u> <u>log</u> for him. _____

6. Can I play <u>with</u> my good <u>pal</u> <u>now</u>? _____

Name _____

A singular noun names one person, place, or thing.

A plural noun names more than one person, place, or thing.

Add **-s** to make most singular nouns plural.

Example: one **cat**  two **cats**

Circle the plural noun in each sentence.

1. Mom has a lot of jobs to do.

2. The kids like to help her.

3. Pam will fix the beds.

4. The dogs have to eat now.

5. Jack does the pots in the sink.

6. Now we can have some eggs.

Turn to a partner. Read each plural noun. Then say each matching singular noun.

Name _____

A plural noun names more than one person, place, or thing.

Add **-es** to form the plural of singular nouns that end with **s**, **ss**, **sh**, **ch**, or **x**.

Example: one **kiss**   two **kisses**

Write a plural noun to complete the sentence. The words in the box and the pictures will help.

| branch | glass | box | dish |

1. Will you help pack the

_____

_ _ _ _ _ _ _ _ _ _ _ _ _

_____?

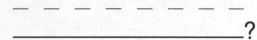

2. This one is for pots and

_____

_ _ _ _ _ _ _ _ _ _ _ _ _

_____.

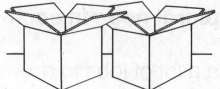

3. That box is for our best

_____

_____.

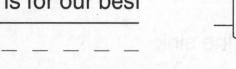

4. What are on the _____?

© Macmillan/McGraw-Hill

Name _____

A sentence begins with a capital letter.
A question ends with a question mark.

Write the questions correctly.

1. who will help me get eggs

_____

- - - - - - - - - - - - - - - - - - - -

_____

2. will the hens peck at me

_____

- - - - - - - - - - - - - - - - - - - -

_____

3. can we go to see the pigs

_____

- - - - - - - - - - - - - - - - - - - -

_____

4. what do little pigs eat

_____

- - - - - - - - - - - - - - - - - - - -

_____

© Macmillan/McGraw-Hill

Name _____

> Add **-s** or **-es** to form the plural of most nouns.
> Begin every sentence with a capital letter. End a
> question with a question mark.

Find the mistakes. Circle the letters that should be capital. Underline the nouns that should be plural. Add the correct end mark.

I. will you help me up

2. who fell on all the egg

3. two cat jumped on me

4. where are they now

5. do you see some leg

6. what is in the two bush

Now write each plural noun correctly.

_____   _____

_ _ _ _ _ _ _   _ _ _ _ _ _ _

_____   _____

_ _ _ _ _ _ _   _ _ _ _ _ _ _

Name _____

Write the plural for each noun.

1. pet _____

2. box _____

3. egg _____

4. dish _____

5. glass _____

6. lunch _____

Write two sentences about how you help at home. Use one or two of the plural nouns you wrote in each sentence. Read your sentences to a partner.

7. _____

8. _____

Name _____

Some plural nouns do not end with **-s** or **-es**. These nouns use a new word to name more than one.

A. Say the nouns and their plurals.

child   children   man   men

goose   geese   mouse   mice

foot   feet

B. Circle the plural or plurals in each group.

1. mouse   man   geese

2. men   foot   child

3. goose   children   feet

4. man   child   mice

Name _____

Some plural nouns use a new word to name more than one.

Choose the plural noun that belongs in each sentence. Write it on the line.

1. The (men, mans) fish at the pond. _____

2. The (children, childs) have a ship. _____

3. They see the prints of many (feet, foots) in the sand.

_____

4. Do (mouses, mice) live here? _____

5. No. The (gooses, geese) live in the pond. _____

Name _____

A sentence begins with a capital letter.

An exclamation ends with an exclamation point.

Find the exclamation in each pair.

Put a check [✓] next to the exclamation.

Circle the exclamation point.
Underline each plural noun.

1. Look at all the mice!
   Where do they live?

2. They live in the man's shop.
   The mice are eating his socks!

3. Stop eating my socks!
   What will the man do?

4. He will bring two cats into the shop.
   Run, mice, run!

© Macmillan/McGraw-Hill

Name _____

Remember that some nouns use new words to name more than one. Begin every sentence with a capital letter. End an exclamation with an exclamation point.

Write C if a sentence is correct.
If a sentence is not correct, circle the mistakes.

1. Don't go in there!

2. the gooses will not like it.

3. that goose is very mad now?

4. Childs, get out quick.

5. She can peck with her bill!

Name _____

Circle the correct plural for each noun.

1. goose

    gooses   geese   geeses

2. foot

    feet   footes   foots

3. man

    men   mans   mens

4. child

    childs   childrens   children

Write the plural for the word in ( ) to complete the sentence.

_____
_ _ _ _ _ _ _ _ _ _ _ _ _ _ _

5. The _____ hid in the grass. (mouse)
        _____

_ _ _ _ _ _ _ _ _ _ _ _ _ _ _

6. Don't step on my _____ ! (foot)

© Macmillan/McGraw-Hill

Name _____

A common noun names any person, pet, place,
or thing. A common noun begins with a lowercase
letter.

A noun that names an exact person, pet, place,
or thing is called a proper noun. A proper noun
begins with a capital letter.

Examples: **Y**an   **J**ill   **T**exas

Write the proper noun in each group.

1. Rick   drum   play   _____

2. kids   Lin   fun   _____

3. cat   let's   Jen   _____

4. Atlanta   hand   pet   _____

Name _____

A proper noun names an exact person or place.
Some proper nouns are more than one word.
Each word in a proper noun begins with a capital
letter.

Miss **P**ink   **W**est **S**treet

Buck **H**ill **S**chool

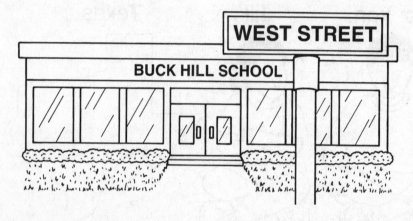

Underline the proper nouns in each sentence.

1. Where is the Land School?

2. It's on Frank Street.

3. Go past Red Duck Pond to get to it.

4. Miss Winn wants to put on a show.

5. Pam will be in the show, too.

6. She used to live in Putnam, Vermont.

Name _____

A proper noun names an exact person or place.
A proper noun begins with a capital letter.

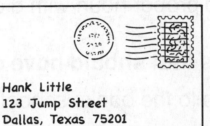

Hank Little
123 Jump Street
Dallas, Texas 75201

Follow the directions to write proper nouns.

1. Write your first and last name.

_____

_____

2. Write your address.

_____

(street) _____

_____

(city, state, zip code) _____

3. Write the name of your school.

_____

_____

4. Write your teacher's name.

_____

_____

Name _____

Begin a proper noun with a capital letter. Some proper nouns are more than one word. Begin each word in a proper noun with a capital letter.

Circle the words that should have capital letters.

I. Al and pam go to the banks school.

2. miss ann has a good band there.

3. "I play the drums," said chan.

4. I got them in a shop on Tip top street.

5. The band will play in new york City.

6. Will nick sing with the band?

Turn to a partner. Say each proper noun on this page.

Then tell your partner some more proper nouns.

Rewrite the sentences. Begin each proper noun with a capital letter.

1. The band is from crest school.

   _____

   _____

2. They come down frost street.

   _____

   _____

3. My pals rick and tan play.

   _____

   _____

4. miss hill and the kids sing.

   _____

   _____

5. They sing three texas songs.

   _____

   _____

Some proper nouns name the days of the week. Some proper nouns name the months. The names of the days and the months begin with capital letters.

Say the days. Circle the capital letters.

Monday   Tuesday   Wednesday

Thursday   Friday   Saturday   Sunday

Say the months. Circle the capital letters.

January   February   March   April

May   June   July   August

September   October   November   December

I. What day do you like best?

_____

_____

2. What month do you like best?

_____

_____

Talk with a partner about your answers to I and 2.

Name _____

Some proper nouns name holidays.
Holiday names begin with capital letters.
Examples: Thanksgiving   Valentine's Day

Draw a line to match the holiday to its picture.

1. Thanksgiving

2. Independence Day
(Fourth of July)

3. Valentine's Day

4. New Year's Day

Name _____

Days, months, and holidays are proper nouns.
All proper nouns begin with capital letters.

Write the word that completes the sentence correctly.

1. Today is _____. (Monday, monday)

2. I do not go to school in _____. (july, July)

3. This flag is for _____.
   (independence Day, Independence Day)

4. We will have lots of fun on _____.
   (Saturday, saturday)

5. Some kids start school in _____.
   (august, August)

Name _____

Begin the names of days, months, and holidays
with capital letters.

**Circle the letters that should be capital. Write the
day, the month, or the holiday correctly.**

1. We liked new year's day. _____

2. That was in january. _____

3. Today is tuesday, February 14. _____

4. It is valentine's Day. _____

5. On monday, we put up little red flags at school.

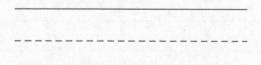

6. What fun things can we
do in march?

Name _____

Underline the name of the day, month or holiday in each sentence. Write <u>C</u> if the name is written correctly. Write <u>NC</u> if the name is not correct. Then write it correctly.

1. We have no school on thursday.

_____

- -

_____

2. It is Thanksgiving.

_____

- -

_____

3. School is out on friday, too.

_____

- -

_____

4. Are you going away in december?

_____

- -

_____

5. We will be back on new year's day.

_____

- -

_____

6. It will be January then.

_____

- -

_____

A verb is a word that shows action.

Examples: Jake **jumps**.   Fran **runs**.

→ **verb** ←

Find the verb in each group. Fill in the circle. The first one is done for you.

1. ○ today
   ◉ ride
   ○ all

2. ○ walk
   ○ oh
   ○ three

3. ○ math
   ○ make
   ○ it

4. ○ who
   ○ some
   ○ eat

5. ○ not
   ○ play
   ○ on

6. ○ go
   ○ of
   ○ many

7. ○ pull
   ○ very
   ○ good

8. ○ now
   ○ help
   ○ me

A verb is a word that shows action.

Write a verb from the box to complete the sentence. The pictures can help.

| pull | jumps | play | wins | run |

_____

1. My pals and I _____ games.

_____

2. We _____ to the gate.

_____

3. Tran _____ over the blocks.

_____

4. Now we can _____!

_____

5. Jane _____ the big race.

© Macmillan/McGraw-Hill

A comma (,) comes after the greeting and after
the closing in a letter.

> Dear Jan, (greeting)
>> I miss you. Do you like where you live now?
>>> Your pal, (closing)
>>> Val

I. Circle the commas after the greeting and closing in this
letter.

> Dear Fred,
>> Can you come to see me Monday?
>>> Your pal,
>>> Rick

2. Put commas after the greeting and closing in this letter.

> Hello Liz
>> I won a big race. It was fun!
>>> Your pal
>>> Ann

**Now write a short letter asking a friend to visit you.
Be sure to include the date, greeting, and closing.**

Use verbs to show action.

Put commas after the greeting and the closing in
a letter.

**This letter is missing two commas and three verbs.
Add the verbs from the box. Add the commas.**

saved	baked	taste

Hello Nan

_____

Mom and I _____ a cake. Then

we _____ some. It was very good. I

_____ some for you in a tin.

Your best pal

Pam

Think of three more verbs. Say them to a partner.

Practice

Name _____

Circle the verb in each sentence. Circle the comma you find.

1. We ride to Gram's.

2. My pal Mack feeds my cat.

3. He walks my dog, too.

4. We sleep on the plane.

5. The plane lands at 6 P.M.

6. I thank Mack for his help.

Write two sentences about how you help your friends. Circle the verbs.

7. _____

_____

8. _____

Talk about your day with a partner. Use verbs. Tell what verbs you used.

Name _____

> The tense of a verb tells when an action happens.
>
> Present-tense verbs tell about action that happens now.
>
> Examples: Dell **makes** a cake.   Pam **helps**.

Circle the verbs in the present tense.
Write them on the lines below.

1. The little boy trips on the rug.

2. He drops his box.

3. The blocks spilled out.

4. Ann rushed over.

5. She puts them back in the box.

_____ _____ _____

- -

_____ _____ _____

Turn to a partner. Say the present-tense verbs from this page aloud. Then take turns saying four more present-tense verbs aloud.

© Macmillan/McGraw-Hill

Name _____

Present-tense verbs tell about action that happens now.

Add **-s** to most verbs to form the present tense.

jump   +   s   =   jumps

Write a present-tense verb to complete each sentence. Add -s to the verb in ( ).

1. Dad _____ care of the plants. (take)

2. His son _____ to help. (want)

3. He _____ the big tin can. (get)

4. He _____ it with water. (fill)

5. Then he _____ it over to Dad. (bring)

Name _____

The important words in a book title begin with a capital letter.

The first word of a book title is always capitalized.

The title of a book is underlined.

Examples: <u>The Girl in the Red Hat</u>

Underline the book title that is correct.

1. Kids help out

Kids Help Out

2. Stan Gets More

stan gets more

3. How Can I Help?

How can I help?

4. Let's get together

Let's Get Together

Practice

Name _____

Grammar:
Present-Tense Verbs

Write <u>C</u> if a sentence or book title is correct. If a sentence or book title is not correct, write the letter or letters to tell how you would make it right.

Ⓐ   Add **-s** to make present-tense verb.

Ⓑ   Capitalize a letter.

Ⓒ   Do not change.

1. He looks at the book.

2. She pick up the dishes.

3. He dig up the land for Mom.

4. the Boy Who Liked Hens

5. He gets the eggs.

Turn to a partner. Find the present-tense verbs on this page. Say them aloud.

Name _____

Make these sentences tell about the present.
Underline the correct verb in ( ).

1. Chan (help, helped, helps) Mom today.

2. He (get, gets, got) a pan for her.

3. Mom (use, used, uses) two eggs.

4. She (adds, added, add) a cup of water.

5. Dad (filled, fills, fill) some glasses with milk.

6. Mom (look, looked, looks) at the clock.

7. Chan (walks, walked, walk) to the bus.

8. He (wave, waves, waved) to Mom and Dad.

Name _____

A past-tense verb tells about action that happened in the past.

Examples: The sun **set**.

The boys **washed** up.

Then they **jumped** into bed.

Put a check next to the sentence that tells about the past. Circle the past-tense verb.

1. Sam made a shape with his hands.

Sam makes a shape with his hands.

2. Chuck watches him.

Chuck watched him.

3. Sam shows Chuck a dog shape.

Sam showed Chuck a dog shape.

With a partner, take turns saying four different past-tense verbs aloud.

Name _____

Past-tense verbs tell about actions that already happened.

Most verbs in the past tense end in **-ed**.

help + ed = helped

**Use a verb from the box to complete the sentence.
Circle the -ed ending in the verb.**

walked   blinked   wanted   pulled   looked

1. I _____ at the sun in my face.

2. Mom _____ down the shade.

3. The cat _____ into the den.

4. We _____ at its shape on the shade.

5. Then the cat _____ to eat.

Name _____

> Future-tense verbs tell about action that is going
> to happen. Add **will** before a verb to form the
> future tense.
>
> I run. ⟶ I will run.
>
> Sometimes you need to drop **-s** from the verb.
>
> She plays. ⟶ She will play.

**Read the story aloud with a partner. Underline the
verbs. Change the verbs to future tense. Write the
future-tense verbs on the lines below.**

Dad and James walk past Fitch Lane. Miss
Chin yells hello. They wave to her. They jump
with her new dog.

1. _____   2. _____

3. _____   4. _____

**Read the story aloud again. Now change all the
verbs to past tense.**

Name _____

> A proper noun begins with a capital letter.
> Examples: **Mike** lived in **Texas**.

Write the sentences. Capitalize the underlined proper nouns.

1. <u>pam</u> will go on a whale watch.

_____

- -

_____

2. She and <u>mom</u> will walk to the dock.

- -

_____

- -

_____

3. They will go on <u>top road</u>.

_____

- -

_____

4. One ship will come from <u>maine</u>.

_____

- -

_____

Now circle all the future-tense verbs in your sentences.

Name _____

Circle all the past-tense verbs.

I. pinched   looks   cares   yelled

2. pats   make   mixed   wished

3. stopped   lived   tapped   jumps

4. liked   pulls   hummed   drinks

5. drag   stopped   used   helped

**Rewrite each sentence to tell about the future.
Change the underlined verb to future tense.**

6. We <u>see</u> the sun come up.

_____

_____

7. The kids <u>play</u> in the shade.

_____

_____

8. Ann and Seth <u>want</u> a drink.

_____

_____

Circle all the proper nouns on this page.

Name _____

The verbs **is** and **are** tell about the present.

Is tells about one person, place, or thing.

Are tells about more than one person, place, or thing.

Examples: Dad **is** there.

   The cats **are** here.

Circle the verb in each sentence. Write <u>1</u> **if the verb tells about one. Write** <u>2</u> **if the verb tells about more than one.**

1. Mom is on the grass.   _____

2. Our two dogs are with her.   _____

3. The twins are in the water.   _____

4. Hal is next to Mom.   _____

5. This game is so much fun!   _____

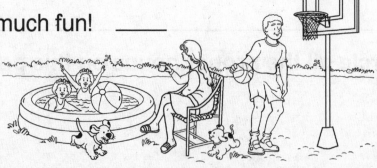

Name _____

Use the verb **is** to tell about one person, place, or thing.

Use the verb **are** to tell about more than one person, place, or thing.

Write is or are to complete each sentence.

1. My things _____ all over the place.

2. Kim _____ here to help.

3. The blocks _____ in the box.

4. My space _____ not a mess now.

Name _____

Every sentence begins with a capital letter. A statement ends with a period. An exclamation ends with an exclamation point.

Write the statements correctly.

1. we are all here

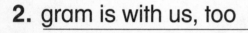

_____

_____

2. gram is with us, too

_____

_____

3. our bags are in the tent

_____

_____

Write the exclamations correctly.

4. see that black stick

_____

_____

5. that is a snake, not a stick

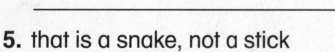

_____

_____

Name _____

**Find the mistakes. Cross out the verb if it is
wrong. Write the correct verb above it.
Circle any letters that should be capital.
Add the correct end mark if one is missing.
(Hint: Each sentence has <u>two mistakes</u>.)**

1. The little kids is in the den _____

2. don't let the dogs in here _____

3. hide the game, quick _____

4. it are too late. _____

5. the dogs is on our game! _____

6. This are not that funny _____

**With a partner, take turns saying sentences
with is or are.**

Name _____

Write <u>is</u> or <u>are</u> to complete each sentence.

1. "It _____ time," Mom said.

2. Jane and I _____ in our best dresses.

3. Giles and Nick _____ in back of us.

4. Giles _____ so funny.

5. Our smiles _____ very, very big!

Write a sentence about your family. Use <u>is</u> or <u>are</u> in the sentence. Read aloud your sentence.

6. _____

Name _____

A contraction is a short way of saying and writing two words.

Two words: **are not**   **does not**

Contractions: **aren't**   **doesn't**

Draw a box around the contractions you find.

1. We can't go skating now.

2. Gram wasn't on the bus.

3. I didn't see her.

4. Why hasn't Gram called?

5. Isn't that Gram?

6. I couldn't find my skates.

Unknown

A contraction is a short form of two words. The two words are put together and letters are left out. An apostrophe (') shows where letters have been left out.

Example: She **isn't** here. (is not = isn't)

Look at the underlined contraction. Circle the two words used to make the contraction.

1. Papa <u>wasn't</u> at his shop. Papa was not at his shop.

2. We <u>didn't</u> go to school. We did not go to school.

3. They <u>aren't</u> walking the dogs. They are not walking the dogs.

4. Gram <u>couldn't</u> ride her bike. Gram could not ride her bike.

5. The buses <u>weren't</u> running. The buses were not running.

Take turns reading each contraction to your partner. Your partner says the two words that make up the contraction.

© Macmillan/McGraw-Hill

Name _____

A contraction is a short form of two words. An apostrophe (') takes the place of letters that are left out to make the contraction.

Write the contraction for the underlined words in each sentence.

1. Splash <u>does not</u> want to help. _____

2. "That <u>is not</u> fun," he said. _____

3. He <u>would not</u> scrub the pans. _____

4. He <u>did not</u> scrape the dishes. _____

5. "You <u>are not</u> going to play," Mom said. _____

A **contraction** is a short way of writing and saying two words.

Use an **apostrophe** (') to take the place of letters that are left out of a contraction.

Circle the contractions that are not correct.
Write the contractions correctly.
Write C if the contraction is correct. _____

1. Mom doesnt' like us to be late. _____

2. You arent going to miss the bus! _____

3. The bus isnt here yet. _____

4. It wasn't on time. _____

5. We are glad it did'nt splash us. _____

Think of two more contractions with a partner.
Say them aloud.

Name _____

Use the words in ( ) to form a contraction. Write the contraction to complete the sentence.

1. Spot _____ in here. (is not)

2. She _____ out in the back. (was not)

3. I _____ see her on the deck. (did not)

4. Spot _____ hide in there. (would not)

5. Why _____ we call her? (do not)

6. We _____ looked in all her hiding places yet. (have not)

Name _____

The verbs **was** and **were** tell about the past.

Was tells about one person, place, or thing.

Were tells about more than one person, place, or thing.

Examples: Little Red **was** in the nest.

Mom and Dad **were** there, too.

Circle the verb that belongs in the sentence.

1. The sun (was, were) up.

2. Three eggs (was, were) in the nest.

3. One egg (was, were) not in the nest.

4. Dad (was, were) away from the nest.

5. Mom and Little Red (was, were) on a branch.

Name _____

Use the verbs **was** and **were** to tell about the past.
Use **was** to tell about one person, place, or thing.
Use **were** to tell about more than one person, place, or thing.

Write <u>was</u> or <u>were</u> to complete the sentence.

I. Our school play _____ today.

2. All the kids _____ in it.

3. Kim and Joe _____ little bugs.

4. I _____ a rose bush.

5. One boy _____ a robin.

6. The funny hats _____ for Kim and Ted.

© Macmillan/McGraw-Hill

Name _____

A proper noun names a special person, place, or thing. A proper noun begins with a capital letter.

Read each row of words. Circle the word or words that should begin with capital letters.

1. girl   fran   joseph

2. mike   she   elm lane

3. hill   grove school   home

4. boy   soon   miss rose

Fill in the blanks to complete the sentences. Use the proper nouns you circled above.

_____   _____

5. _____ and _____ were on

_____. They were

walking to _____.

6. We met _____ at the bus stop.

With a partner, take turns saying more sentences. Use proper nouns and the verbs <u>was</u> and <u>were</u>.

Name _____

Use **was** to tell about one.

Use **were** to tell about more than one.

Capitalize proper nouns.

Find four mistakes in the story.
Circle the sentences with mistakes.
Write the sentences correctly on the lines.

Hal lives on plum lane. Jon came to play. The two boys

was out back. They saw a robin in a nest. Lots of bugs

were in the grass. One bug were not nice. It bit hal on the

nose!

_____

I. _____

_____

2. _____

_____

3. _____

_____

4. _____

Name _____

Circle and write <u>was</u> or <u>were</u> to complete each sentence.

1. Six white gulls _____ on the sand.

   was   were

2. One gull _____ on the post.

   was   were

3. Some fish _____ under the water.

   was   were

4. The gull's bill _____ opened wide.

   was   were

5. That _____ a big splash!

   was   were

Take turns with a partner saying sentences with <u>was</u> or <u>were</u>.

The verbs **has** and **have** tell about the present.

Has tells about one person, place, or thing.

Have tells about more than one person, place, or thing.

Examples: Lulu **has** an old glass.

Pru and Zack **have** some cans.

Underline the verb if it tells about one.
Circle the verb if it tells about more than one.

1. The kids have work to do.

2. Pru has a black bag for cans.

3. Zack has lots of cans.

4. Lulu and Dad have glass things.

5. The two girls have big piles of stuff.

With a partner, think of two more sentences that tell about the pictures. Use <u>has</u> and <u>have</u> in your sentences.

Name _____

Use the verb **has** to tell about one person, place, or thing.

Use the verb **have** to tell about more than one person, place, or thing.

Match parts to write a sentence about the pictures. Then circle the verb in each sentence.

My pal Chan	have fun together.
Your bag	has a big hole in it.
Ann and Bill	have string on them.
The two piles	has a box of games.

I. _____

_____

2. _____

_____

3. _____

_____

4. _____

© Macmillan/McGraw-Hill

Name _____

Every sentence begins with a capital letter.

A statement ends with a period.

A question ends with a question mark.

Write each sentence correctly.

1. what is in Joe's box

_____

- -

_____

2. joe has pine cones for us

- -

_____

3. can we hang them with string

_____

- -

_____

4. now the birds can eat here

_____

- -

_____

Name _____

Find the mistakes in the story.

A Change the verb to **has** or **have**.

B Begin with a capital letter.

C Add an end mark.

D Do not change.

(1) Some people do not care about our land (2) do you see all the junk on the sand? (3) Now, Carlos and Rosa has to pick it up. (4) doesn't the sand look good now (5) Carlos and Rosa have cans and glass to take home. (6) Mom have a good use for them.

For each sentence in the story, write the letter or letters that tell how you would fix the mistake.

1. _____   2. _____

3. _____   4. _____

5. _____   6. _____

Name _____

Write <u>has</u> or <u>have</u> to complete each sentence.

_____
- - - - - - - - - - - - - - - -

1. He _____ a pile of used papers.

_____
- - - - - - - - - - - - - - - -

2. They all _____ a blank side.

_____
- - - - - - - - - - - - - - - -

3. Tekla _____ a good plan.

_____
- - - - - - - - - - - - - - - -

4. We _____ some brushes.

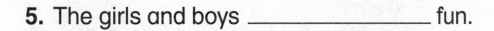

_____
- - - - - - - - - - - - - - - -

5. The girls and boys _____ fun.

Think of two more sentences that tell about the pictures on this page. Use <u>has</u> and <u>have</u>. Say your sentences to a partner.

The verbs **go** and **do** have different forms to tell about the present and the past.

Present	**Past**
He **goes**. We **go**.	We all **went**.
She **does**. They **do**.	We all **did**.

Write the verb that tells about the present.

1. Jay _____ outside to play. (goes, went)

2. Al _____ not like to splash. (does, did)

3. We _____ have fun in the rain. (do, did)

Write the verb that tells about the past.

4. When _____ the sun come out? (does, did)

5. May and Lulu _____ for a walk. (go, went)

6. I _____ in when it got cold. (go, went)

© Macmillan/McGraw-Hill

Name _____

The verbs **go** and **do** have different forms for the present tense and the past tense.

Present: **go, goes**   **do, does**

Past: **went**   **did**

A. Underline the present-tense forms of <u>go</u> or <u>do</u>. Circle the past-tense forms of <u>go</u> or <u>do</u>.

1. The rain goes plop, plop, plop!

2. Did you hear that great big clap?

3. Why does it have to rain so much?

4. The lights went out.

5. What will we do now?

B. With a partner, take turns saying four sentences about the weather. Use the past tense of <u>go</u> or <u>do</u>.

C. Then say four more sentences about the weather. Use the present tense of <u>go</u> or <u>do</u>.

Name _____

Begin proper nouns with capital letters. If the
name of a person or place is more than one word,
capitalize all the important words.

Sam Shade   Flop the Fish

**Circle the letters that should be capital. Write the
proper nouns correctly.**

1. tank the tiger went
   outside with his son.
   _____
   _ _ _ _ _ _ _ _ _ _ _ _ _ _ _ _
   _____

2. "See how the sun goes
   in and out," sal stripe said.
   _____
   _ _ _ _ _ _ _ _ _ _ _ _ _ _ _ _
   _____

3. I do not like the sound of
   the wind," said papa ape.
   _____
   _ _ _ _ _ _ _ _ _ _ _ _ _ _ _ _
   _____

4. "The air does have a chill,"
   said snap the Snake.
   _____
   _ _ _ _ _ _ _ _ _ _ _ _ _ _ _ _
   _____

5. "Did anyone watch the
   news?" Mama ape said.
   _____
   _ _ _ _ _ _ _ _ _ _ _ _ _ _ _ _
   _____

© Macmillan/McGraw-Hill

Name _____

The verbs **go** and **do** use different forms to tell about the present and the past. The names of people and places begin with capital letters.

Read the story. Circle four sentences with mistakes. Write the sentences correctly.

One day, West Wind goed wild. west wind gave a yell.

"I'll make it cold!" he yelled. "That will be fun." Sunray

was upset. It do not sound like fun to her. So sunray

shined a lot. Soon it got very warm. "Now that's fun!"

she said.

1. _____

2. _____

3. _____

4. _____

A. Underline a form of the verbs <u>go</u> or <u>do</u> in each sentence. Write <u>present</u> or <u>past</u> to tell the tense of the underlined verb.

1. My cat never goes out in

_____

- - - - - - - - - - - - - - - - - -

the rain. _____

- - - - - - - - - - - - - - - - - - -

2. She goes under the chair to hide. _____

- - - - - - - - - - - - - - - - - -

3. My dogs go out anyway. _____

- - - - - - - - - - - - - - - - - - -

4. They went out when Mom came in. _____

- - - - - - - - - - - - - - - - - -

5. We did a good job with the towels! _____

B. With a partner, say two more sentences about the pictures. Use a form of the verbs <u>do</u> or <u>go</u> in each sentence.

© Macmillan/McGraw-Hill

Name _____

The verb **see** has a special form to tell about the past.

Present	**Past**
She **sees**. We **see**.	They **saw**.

Circle the verb that tells about the past.

1. Jean (see, sees, saw) the leaf.

2. We (see, sees, saw) a small bug.

3. Pat (see, sees, saw) many lines on the leaf.

Circle the verb that tells about the present.

4. Sue (see, sees, saw) spots on the leaf.

5. Pat and Sue (see, sees, saw) a bug.

6. We also (see, sees, saw) the bug.

Name _____

The verb **see** has different forms for the present tense and the past tense.

Present: **see, sees**

Past: **saw**

Circle sentences that tell about the present. Underline sentences that tell about the past.

I. We saw a play about Ben Franklin.

2. Ben cannot see well.

3. "I saw an eye doctor," Ben said.

4. Will saw that it was raining outside.

5. "I see that the kite is wet from the rain!"

With a partner, say two more sentences about the play. Use the present tense and past tense of the verb <u>see</u>.

© Macmillan/McGraw-Hill

Name _____

Use commas in a letter
- after the greeting and the closing,
- between the day and year in a date,
- between the name of a city and state.

Circle the commas in this letter.

June 30, 1752

Dear Peter,

My idea worked. I said it would. Come
see me in Philadelphia, Pennsylvania.

Your friend,

Ben

Add the missing commas in this letter.

May 10 1815

Dear Granddad

Do you like living in Bath Maine?
Mom said we can visit soon.

Your best girl

Lena

Write a short letter to a friend. Use commas.

Read the letter.

Two commas are missing. Three verbs are wrong.

Add the missing commas. Cross out the verbs that are wrong.

Write the verbs in the correct tense on the lines below.

September 3 1922

Dear Nana,

    Dad put up a little house in our elm tree. "It's a bat house," he said.

    Last Monday, my friends came over. We see five bats go in the house. We sees the bats hanging upside down.

    I said, "Bats are fun to saw."

      Your grandson

      Joe

Name _____

A. Write the correct tense of <u>see</u> to complete each sentence.

1. Today Mom said, "You should _____ this."

2. Yesterday Al and Jo _____ Mom bake muffins.

3. Today they _____ her cook rice.

4. "We _____ Dad do that once," they said.

5. Now Al _____ steam rise up.

6. "I _____ the rice cook," Jo said finally.

B. Say two more sentences to a partner. Use the past tense of <u>see</u>. Write your sentences.

7. _____

8. _____

An **adverb** is a word that tells more about a verb in a sentence. A verb tells about action. An adverb can tell when an action happened.

Examples: Tim ran **first.** Lin came **next. Then** Jake ran.

adverb

Read the story. Underline the adverbs that tell when.

Big Bunny said, "Who opened my box today?"

First Skunk said, "I did not do it."

Next Frog said, "I did not see who did it."

Baby Bunny soon ran by.

Then she said, "Thank you for my new toy!"

Now write your own sentences.
Use three adverbs that tell when from this page.
Say your sentence to a partner.

_____

4. _____

_____

5. _____

_____

6. _____

An **adverb** is a word that tells more about a verb in a sentence. An adverb can tell when an action happened.

Sometimes an adverb is next to a verb.

Example: Rob sang **yesterday**.

Sometimes an adverb is not next to a verb.

Example: **Now** liz sings

Find the adverb in each sentence.
Write <u>Yes</u> if the adverb is next to a verb.
Write <u>No</u> if the adverb is not next to a verb.

1. Dad read a story to Jan yesterday. _____

2. First Little Spot cleaned the floor. _____

3. "Now clean the cups," said Mama Spot. _____

4. "I will wash the plates next," _____

   said Little Spot. _____

5. "I finally like this story," said Jan. _____

Name _____

An **apostrophe** (') takes the place of the **o** in **contractions** formed with **not**.

Example: have + not = haven't

Write a contraction for the two words in ( ).

1. "I _____ think Bumpy is home," Sandy said. (do not)

2. "He _____ in here taking a bath," said Big Green Frog. (is not)

3. "He _____ jump in the pond for a swim," said White Swan. (did not)

4. Bumpy _____ anywhere Sandy looked. (was not)

Name _____

Make a check mark [✔] next to the sentence with an adverb that tells when an action takes place. Circle the adverb. Underline the contraction.

1. The fox woke early to get the grapes.

2. The fox couldn't get the grapes.

3. Then the fox was mad.

4. "I will get those grapes now," he said.

5. But he wasn't there on time.

6. A crow ate all the grapes first!

Make up more of the story with a partner. Take turns saying four more sentences that use adverbs that tell when actions happen.

© Macmillan/McGraw-Hill

Name _____

Write the adverb that tells <u>when</u> in each sentence.

1. Bunny cut his hair today. _____

2. "You did not ask Mom first," said Fox. _____

3. Then Mom was mad. _____

Mark the contraction for the underlined words.

4. "I <u>do not</u> like it," Mom said.

   ○ won't   ○ don't   ○ doesn't

5. "You <u>have not</u> got any hair!," Bear said.

   ○ can't   ○ hasn't ○ haven't

6. "It <u>does not</u> matter to me," said Bunny.

   ○ don't   ○ didn't   ○ doesn't

Name _____

An **adjective** is a word that tells about a noun.
A **noun** is a person, place, or thing.

That is a **great** painting.

adjective   noun

A. **Circle the adjective in each sentence. Underline the noun it tells about. The first one is done for you.**

1. The boat is sailing on a(blue) sea.

2. A little girl stands on the deck.

3. The cool wind blows her hair.

4. The tall sails flap in the wind.

5. People wave from a sandy beach.

B. **With a partner, say three more sentences about the picture. Use three adjectives.**

An **adjective** is a word that tells about a noun.
Some adjectives tell what kind. Some adjectives
tell how many.

Examples: <u>**What kind**</u>   <u>**How many**</u>
              a **nice** boy   **three** girls
              the **silly** dog   **many** cats

**Circle the adjectives that tell what kind.
Underline the adjectives that tell how many.**

I. Those are cute pigs.

2. I used pink clay to
shape them.

3. What funny tails those
pigs have!

4. Who made the two ducks?

5. This hen has some chicks.

6. This little chick keeps falling down.

Name _____

> The name of a special person or place is a **proper noun.** Proper nouns begin with capital letters.

A. **Circle the proper noun in each sentence. Write it correctly on the line.**

_____

1. val has some sand and a glass jar. _____

_____

2. Is the sand from jones beach? _____

_____

3. No, mother got it at a little shop. _____

_____

4. The shop is on main street. _____

B. **With a partner, say two more sentences about the picture. Use adjectives that tell about color.**

Name _____

A. Read the letter. Circle seven words that should begin with capital letters. Remember that the pronoun I is always a capital letter.

Dear mike,

   Would you like to come to the

shoat Gallery with us? It is on

front street in the city. dad says

we will see some great paintings

there. i hope you can come!

     Your friend,

     Sandy wan

B. Write the sentence correctly. Add an adjective to tell more about the underlined nouns.

The <u>girl</u> who painted that <u>daisy</u> is joan reed.

_____

- -

_____

- -

_____

Name _____

Write an adjective to tell about the underlined noun.

_____

- - - - - - - - - - - - - - - -

1. Who made that _____ quilt?

_____

- - - - - - - - - - - - - - - -

2. It has _____ squares.

_____

- - - - - - - - - - - - - - - -

3. Look at the _____ sheep.

_____

- - - - - - - - - - - - - - - -

4. A _____ sound scared them.

_____

- - - - - - - - - - - - - - - -

5. The sheep ran down the _____ hill.

_____

- - - - - - - - - - - - - - - -

6. Now the _____ girl can't find them.

Name _____

Add **-er** to an adjective to compare two people, places, or things.

Example: Jon is **faster** than Mike.

Add **-est** to an adjective to compare three or more people, places, or things.

Example: Ed is the **fastest** boy on the team.

A. Write the adjectives that compare.

add <u>-er</u>	add <u>-est</u>

I. low

2. sweet

3. kind

B. Underline the adjectives that compare.

4. My dog is slower than Tim's dog.

5. It is bigger than Pedro's train.

6. It is the cutest dog in the bunch.

Name _____

> Add **-er** to an adjective to compare two people, places, or things.
>
> Add **-est** to an adjective to compare three or more people, places, or things.

Write the adjective that completes the sentence correctly.

1. Of all our kites, Al's has the _____ tail.

   longer   **longest**

2. This is the _____ spot in the whole park.

   highest   **high**

3. The wind is _____ now than before.

   strong   **stronger**

4. Kim's kite is _____ than my kite.

   newer   **newest**

5. Mine is the _____ kite of all in the sky.

   big   **biggest**

Name _____

Every sentence begins with a capital letter.
Every sentence ends with a special mark.

A. Circle the sentence that is correct.

1. which plane has longer wings?

   Which plane has longer wings?

2. My plane can fly over the tallest tree.

   my plane can fly over the tallest tree

3. His plane is lighter than yours.

   his plane is lighter than yours?

4. Is that the fastest plane of all

   Is that the fastest plane of all?

**B. With a partner, say all the adjectives that
compare in the sentences. Then use two
adjectives that compare in two more sentences.**

Meet Ben Franklin
Grade I/Unit 5

© Macmillan/McGraw-Hill

Name _____

Find the word in the second sentence that means the same as the underlined word. Write both words on the lines.

1. Mom told me to put on my <u>hat</u>.

   This cap will block the sun.

   _____

   -

2. My <u>job</u> is to dig up the dirt.

   It is hard work.

   _____

   -

Find the word that means the opposite of the underlined word. Write both words.

3. We got an <u>early</u> start.

   We worked until it was late.

   -

   _____

4. Look at how <u>big</u> the plant has grown.

   It came from such a little seed.

   -

   _____

© Macmillan/McGraw-Hill

Name _____

Look for mistakes with adjectives that compare. Look for mistakes with capital letters and end marks.

Write X if a sentence has any mistakes.

Write C if a sentence is correct.

_____

- - - - - - - -

1. what makes the sticks fly up _____

   - - - - - - - - -

2. You have to roll and push. _____

3. Which of the three sticks will spin for the long time

   - - - - - - - - -

   of all? _____

   _____

   - - - - - - - -

4. Ruby's stick makes a <u>soft</u> sound than mine does. _____

   - - - - - - - -

5. Catch the stick before it drops! _____

   - - - - - - - -

6. my stick has a wider top than yours _____

© Macmillan/McGraw-Hill

Name _____

A. Circle the adjectives that compare in the sentences.
   Write 2 if the adjective compares two.
   Write 3 if the adjective compares three or more.

1. Lee has the newest bike of all. _____

2. The lighter bike belongs to Pam. _____

3. This bus is bigger than that bus. _____

4. The oldest boat broke down. _____

5. The smallest plane landed first. _____

6. Which of those trains is longer? _____

7. The fastest sled dog leads the pack. _____

B. Talk with a partner about things in your
   classroom. Use adjectives that compare two
   and adjectives that compare three or more.

© Macmillan/McGraw-Hill

Name _____

Words that have the same or almost the same meaning are called **synonyms**.

> **Synonyms:**   smile   grin
>
>   shine   glow

Words that have opposite meanings are called **antonyms**.

> **Antonyms:**   new   old
>
>   up   down

Read each row of words.

Circle the two words that are synonyms.

1. kind   happen   nice   ground

2. tiny   plant   big   little

3. happy   glad   mean   grow

Circle the two words that are antonyms.

4. dig   before   after   from

5. all   seeds   nothing   green

6. wet   care   again   dry

© Macmillan/McGraw-Hill

A **contraction** is a short way of saying and writing two words. Many contractions are formed with **not**. An **apostrophe**(') takes the place of the letters that are left out.
Examples: do + not = don't
does + not = doesn't

A. Match the underlined words to contractions. Write the sentence letter on the line. The first one is done for you.

a. This <u>is not</u> the shortest stick.

b. They <u>are not</u> taller than me.

c. I <u>did not</u> color the smoothest apple.

d. He <u>was not</u> the loudest one.

e. We <u>were not</u> the fastest runners.

f. We <u>could not</u> see the smaller bug.

1. isn't _____a_____   **2.** couldn't _____

3. wasn't _____   **4.** weren't _____

5. didn't _____   **6.** aren't _____

B. Read the sentences aloud again. Tell a partner an antonym for all the adjectives that compare.

A. Read the words. Write a synonym and an antonym for each word.

	Synonym	Antonym
1. big		
2. short		
3. smooth		
4. quick		
5. joyful		

B. Work with a partner. Say a sentence for a synonym in your list. Then say the same sentence with its antonym. Keep going until you use all your synonyms and antonyms.

Name _____

Read the story.

Write <u>S</u> if the underlined words in each part are synonyms.

Write <u>A</u> if the underlined words are antonyms.

The <u>little</u> plant wanted to be as <u>big</u> as the other plants

----

in the garden. _____

He tried to <u>stretch</u> his stem, but he couldn't <u>reach</u> up

----

any higher. _____

"I don't like being <u>short</u>," he said. "I want to be <u>tall</u>

----

now." _____

"Wait," his sister said. "The sun will shine on you.
Rain will fall and soak the <u>dirt</u>. You will drink in the
water and other good things from the <u>ground</u>. Then you

----

will grow." _____

"Is there a <u>faster</u> way? " he said.

"There's no <u>quicker</u> way," she said.

_____

Name _____

An **adjective** tells about a noun. Some adjectives tell the color of something.

Example: **blue** sky

Some adjectives are words for numbers.

Examples: **one** (1)   **two** (2)   **three** (3)

Underline the adjective that tells about color in each sentence. Circle the number words. Draw a line to the bike it tells about.

1. The baby's pink bike has three wheels.

2. Pam's tan bike has two wheels.

3. She rides a red bike with one wheel.

4. There are four wheels on the green bike.

5. See six black wheels go round and round.

Name _____

Some adjectives tell what color something is.

Some adjectives tell a number or how many.

A. Write a color word or a number word from the box to complete the sentences. Use each word only one time.

one	two	blue	red

1. What can your new _____ robot do?

2. It made me this _____ scarf.

3. It can drive _____ machine.

4. It can fix _____ wheels on my cart.

B. With a partner, use the color words and number words in the box in four new sentences.

Name _____

Contractions that are formed with the word **not**
use an apostrophe (') to take the place of the
letter **o**.

A. Write the sentences.
   Replace the underlined
   words with a contraction.

1. The yellow bus <u>was not</u> on time.

_____

_____

2. We <u>could not</u> get to the white tent.

_____

_____

3. The boys' blue bikes <u>are not</u> here.

_____

_____

4. I <u>do not</u> need my green ticket.

_____

_____

B. Find the adjectives that tell about color on this
   page. Say them to a partner in new sentences.

Read the story. Circle the color words. Underline the number words.

One black cat wasn't happy. He didn't like having six mice in his house. "I will catch those mice," he said.

"We don't want that to happen," the little gray mice said. But the cat had four soft feet. The mice couldn't tell when he was coming. So they made three alarms.

When the cat came down the five red steps in front of their home, three green bells rang. The mice hid. "The cat can't catch us!" they said.

Name _____

**A. Circle the color word in ( ) to complete
the sentence.**

1. Mr. Whiz put on a (white, hat, long) coat.

2. He got into his (see, like, blue) machine.

3. The (square, hard, green) screen lit up.

4. One of the (pink, low, two) lights blinked.

**B. Circle the number word in ( ) to complete the
sentence.**

5. He pulled the (little, two, go) switches.

6. (Dry, Four, What) loud pops filled the air.

7. There were (red, loud, five) flashes.

8. He flew for (ten, black, low) hours in space.

Name _____

A **preposition** connects one part of a sentence to another. Some prepositions tell more about a noun or a pronoun.

Example: The picture **on** the wall is mine.

Some prepositions tell more about a verb.

Example: We will walk **to** the store.

for	with	across	in

A. Complete the sentences with a preposition from the box.

1. I go to school _____ my friend.

2. We went _____ the tent when it rained.

3. Kim ran _____ the street to the other side.

4. Mom has a present _____ Grandpa.

B. Use each preposition from the box in a new sentence. Tell your sentences to a partner.

Name _____

Some **prepositional phrases** tell more about a noun or pronoun. Others tell about verbs. Each phrase starts with a preposition. There are no verbs in a prepositional phrase

Examples: The coat **on the chair** is mine. Bret took a muffin **off the plate**.

Underline the prepositional phrase in the sentences.

1. Six kids on the team are here.

2. Coach Pedro talked to the team.

3. Marta ran with her team.

4. Sara fell on the grass.

5. Ellen was behind the others.

6. Carlos beat the runners in a race.

© Macmillan/McGraw-Hill

Name _____

The days of the week are proper nouns. The
names of the days begin with capital letters.

Write the word that is correct.

1. Mark can do just one spin on

_____

_____

thurs.   **Thursday**   thursday

_____

2. He tried to do three spins on _____.
Tuesday   **tues**   tuesday

_____

3. He fell down six times on _____.
wed.   **wednesday**   **Wednesday**

_____

4. By _____, he can spin four times.
fri.   **friday**   **Friday**

5. He spins five times on

_____

_____

sun.   **Sunday**   sunday

A. Circle the preposition in ( ) to complete each sentence.

1. Liza gets tickets (blue, to, short) the big show.

2. Harry wants to know (about, see, two) the show.

3. The family takes the bus (some, across, ticket) town.

4. Their seats are right (by, sit, where) the stage.

5. The man keeps six pins (last, try, in) the air.

6. The elephants march (big, quick, around) the stage.

7. A clown does a trick (behind, later, slow) Mom's head.

8. Liza will try the trick (long, at, like) her home.

B. Use the prepositions you found in new sentences. Tell them to a partner.

Name _____

Write the best prepositional phrase from the box to complete each sentence. Cross out the days of the week that are not written correctly.

off her seat	without his hat
in the air	of blocks

1. Three birds flew _____ on sunday.

2. Two bags _____ came on monday.

3. Dad left _____ on Wednesday.

4. She fell _____ on thursDay.

Name _____

A sentence is made up of parts.

The **subject** of a sentence is the part that tells **whom** or **what** the sentence is about.

Example: An ant is on the leaf.

What is on the leaf?

An ant is. **An ant** is the subject.

Answer the question to find the subject of each sentence. Write the subject.

I. Flies have wings. _____

_ _ _ _ _ _ _ _ _ _ _ _ _ _ _ _ _ _ _ _

What has wings? _____

2. That tiny spider made a big web. _____

_ _ _ _ _ _ _ _ _ _ _ _ _ _ _ _ _ _ _ _

What made a big web? _____

3. Mr. Jones takes care of bees. _____

_ _ _ _ _ _ _ _ _ _ _ _ _ _ _ _ _ _ _ _

Who takes care of bees? _____

Use the subjects you found in new sentences. Say them to a partner.

Name _____

The **subject** of a sentence tells **whom** or **what** the sentence is about.

Example: **Pam** knows about bugs.

The **predicate** tells what the subject does.

Example: Two moths **fly around the light.**

Make each sentence tell about the picture. Choose a subject or predicate from the box. Write it on the line.

jumps in the grass	march up the hill
A butterfly	Many bees

1. _____ live in the hive.

2. Six little ants _____.

3. _____ lands on the rose.

4. A grasshopper _____.

Name _____

> A sentence begins with a capital letter and ends
> with a special mark.

Write each sentence correctly.

1. where is my friend Fuzzy

_____

_ _

_____

2. little Ant does not know

_____

_ _

_____

3. is Fuzzy in that silky case

_____

_ _

_____

4. fuzzy is a now a butterfly

_____

_ _

_____

Read each sentence aloud to a partner.
Say the subject of each sentence.

Name _____

Read the story. Then write the letter or letters to tell how to fix each numbered sentence.

Ⓐ Add a subject.　　　　Ⓒ Add an end mark.

Ⓑ Begin with a capital letter.　　Ⓓ Do not change.

　　(1) ant and White Bird didn't get along. (2) One day, Ant fell into the water (3) White Bird dropped a leaf into the water (4) Got on the leaf. (5) The wind pushed the leaf to the sand. (6) Ant was saved. (7) What happened to Ant and White Bird (8) Have become good friends.

1. _____　　2. _____　　3. _____

4. _____　　5. _____　　6. _____

7. _____　　8. _____

Circle the subject in each sentence.

1. Some bugs live in the ground.

2. That dirt pile is an ant hill.

3. Ants live inside.

Circle the predicate in each sentence.

4. Henry likes to watch ants.

5. This store sells ant farms.

Write a subject to complete each sentence.

6. A tiny _____ is on the leaf.

7. _____ likes all kinds of bugs.

Write a predicate to complete each sentence.

8. A caterpillar _____.

9. An ant _____.

A pronoun is a word that takes the place of a noun. Use the pronouns **she**, **he**, **it**, or **they** to take the place of one or more people or things in the subject of a sentence.

<u>Mark and Manish</u> have a dog. **They** have a dog.

Use the pronouns **her**, **him**, **it**, or **them** to take the place of one or more people or things in the object of a sentence.

I asked <u>Zaneb</u> for a book. I asked **her** for a book.

Circle the pronoun that takes the place of the underlined part of the sentence.

1. <u>Janet</u> likes to run and play. She   It

2. <u>Ari</u> likes to throw the ball. They   He

3. Misha writes <u>a book report</u>. her   it

4. Anna and Geir sell <u>hats</u>. them   it

5. <u>Elena</u> is my best friend. They   She

A **pronoun** is a word that takes the place of a noun.

Example: **The ship** went to the moon.

              It went to the moon.

Write a pronoun from the box in place of the underlined words.

He	It	She	They	We

1. Our class learned about space. _____

2. The space ship landed on the moon. _____

3. Two people got out of their ship. _____

4. The man walked on the moon. _____

5. The woman picked up moon rocks. _____

Say a sentence about a space ship. Your partner can use a pronoun in place of the noun you say in a new sentence.

© Macmillan/McGraw-Hill

Name _____

The pronoun *I* is always a capital letter.

Examples: **I** went to my sister's party.
Sis liked the card **I** gave her.

Read the story. Cross out the pronoun *I* when it is not written correctly.

I gave Sis a book about space for her birthday. She liked the book i gave her. i wanted her to read it to me. "Not now," Sis said. "But i really want to hear it," i said. "You have to wait until the party is over," Sis told me. I felt sad, but i waited. Later, Sis read me the book. "This is a great present," i shouted. "i love it, too," agreed Sis.

Name _____

A. Read the sentences. Read the pronouns. Underline the word or words in each sentence that the pronoun can replace.

1. Jack made Dad a card.   **He**

2. Dad loved the card.   **it**

3. Jack and Dad read the card together.   **They**

4. Mom wanted to see the card.   **She**

5. Mom told Jack that she wanted a card, too.   **him**

6. Jack made more cards for Dad and Mom.   **them**

B. Say two more sentences about Jack, Mom, and Dad to a partner. Your partner says a pronoun that takes the place of some words in each sentence. Then your partner says two more sentences. You say the pronoun that takes the place of some words in each sentence.

Mark the correct pronoun to take the place of the underlined subject.

1. <u>Kim and her dad</u> watch from the ground.
   ○ He   ○ It
   ○ They

2. <u>Kim's mom</u> is on that space ship.
   ○ We   ○ She
   ○ It

3. <u>Dan Burns</u> is on this trip, too.
   ○ They   ○ I
   ○ He

4. <u>Kim's mom and Dan</u> look out the window.
   ○ They   ○ She
   ○ We

5. <u>Earth</u> looks beautiful from space.
   ○ He   ○ It
   ○ We

Name _____

A **pronoun** is a word that takes the place of a noun.

Use the pronouns **he**, **she**, or **it** to take the place of one person or thing in the subject of a sentence.

> Pete is a cook. **He** is a good cook.

Use the pronoun **they** to take the place of more than one person or thing in the subject.

> The girls sing. **They** sing very well.

Circle the pronoun that takes the place of the underlined part of the sentence.

1. Mom and Dad work. They work hard.

2. Mr. Wall fixes cars. He fixes old cars.

3. Anna sells hats. She sells bags, too.

4. The two girls walk dogs. They walk all kinds of dogs.

5. My sister makes dresses. She makes doll dresses.

> A **pronoun** is a word that takes the place of a noun.

Write the sentence. Use a pronoun from the box in place of the underlined subject.

He	She	It	They

I. <u>Mrs. Hook</u> makes clay dolls.

_____

2. <u>Her sister and friend</u> make them, too.

_____

3. <u>The red clay</u> gets very hard.

_____

4. <u>Dad</u> buys a doll for Mom.

_____

_____

With a partner, say two more sentences about the clay dolls. Then use a pronoun from the box in place of the subject of each sentence.

Name _____

Use a comma

- between the day and year in a date.
- between the name of a city and state.
- after the greeting and closing in a letter.

Put commas where they belong.

1. Mom left her old job on May 16 2004.
2. She got a new job in Dayton Ohio.
3. June 19 2004

Dear Granddad

    Mom loves her job. She is very happy. Mr. Walker is her new boss. He said Mom is the best worker in the whole place.

               Your grandson

               Marco

Write a short letter from Granddad to Marco. Do not use pronouns. Have a partner rewrite the letter with pronouns in place of some subjects. Read the two letters out loud.

Correct the letter. Cross out the underlined words. Write a pronoun to take their place in the space above. Add missing commas.

March 14 1874

Dear Will,

   Our new house is done. Our new house is made of logs. Dad used tree trunks to make the logs. Dad had to cut down lots of trees.

   My sister Kate has her own room now. My sister Kate is very happy about that.

   Next week, Mom and Dad will open their shop in Dows Iowa. Mom and Dad will sell food, cloth, and other goods.

                    Your best friend

                    Hans

Name _____

**Rewrite the sentence.
Write a pronoun for the
underlined subject.**

1. My dad has a friend named Willie.

_____

- -

_____

2. Willie has a fun job.

_____

- -

_____

3. His job is to make children laugh.

_____

- -

_____

4. Penny works with Willie.

_____

- -

_____

5. Penny and Willie are clowns.

_____

- -

_____

© Macmillan/McGraw-Hill

Name _____

The words **I** and **me** are pronouns.

Use **I** in the subject of a sentence.

Use **me** in the predicate of a sentence.

Examples: **I** have a book about Baby Bird.
             Mom gave **me** the book.

Write <u>I</u> in the subject.

1. _____ am Baby Bird.

2. My sisters and _____ just hatched.

3. _____ want some food.

Write <u>me</u> in the predicate.

4. Mom feeds worms to _____.

5. She keeps _____ warm in the nest.

6. Soon, Dad will show _____ how to fly.

© Macmillan/McGraw-Hill

Name _____

Use the pronoun **I** in the subject of a sentence.

Use the pronoun **me** in the predicate of a sentence.

Choose the pronoun from ( ) that belongs in the sentence. Write it on the line.

1. _____ want to learn about deer. (I, me)

2. Mom helps _____ learn. (I, me)

3. She reads _____ facts about deer. (I, me)

4. _____ learn that a baby deer is called a fawn. (I, me)

5. Mom shows _____ a fawn's spots. (I, me)

With a partner, say two more sentences using *I* and *me*.

Name _____

The pronoun **I** is always a capital letter.

Example: **I** have a new puppy.

Complete each sentence with I.

1. _____ got a puppy
from my Mom and Dad.

2. _____ named my puppy Flop.

3. Dad and _____ teach Flop to fetch.

4. Every day, _____ watch Flop grow bigger and
bigger.

5. _____ think Flop
is too big for his bed.

6. Mom and _____
buy Flop a new bed.

Name _____

Use **I** in the subject of a sentence.

Use **me** in the predicate of a sentence.

Always capitalize the pronoun **I**.

Find mistakes in the play. Circle the pronoun <u>I</u> if it is not written correctly. Draw an <u>X</u> on <u>I</u> or <u>me</u> if it is not used correctly.

1. CUBBY: Mama catches fish for I.

Sometimes, i eat berries, too.

I am getting taller and stronger.

2. NUBBY: Me want to learn to fish, Mama.

Cubby and i are growing up.

3. MAMA: i will teach you to fish, sons.

You will watch me and learn.

Circle the pronoun that belongs in the sentence. Write it on the line.

1. _____ went to see our new baby horse.

   Me   I

2. Dad tells _____ it is called a colt.

   me   I

3. Dad and _____ watch the colt try to stand.

   I   me

4. _____ will watch the colt grow up.

   I   Me

5. One day, the colt will be friends with _____.

   I   me

With a partner say four more sentences about the colt. Use the pronouns *I* and *me*.

An **adverb** is a word that tells more about a verb in a sentence. A verb tells about action. An adverb can tell how an action happened. Many adverbs end in *-ly*.

Examples: Henry spoke **sadly**.
              Jane smiled **happily**.

Read the story. Find the adverbs and write them on the lines. Then use the adverbs in more sentences. Say your sentences to a partner.

My family made a fort. Papa pounded the nails loudly with his hammer. Nana carried wood carefully. Maria sawed the wood quickly. I painted the fort slowly, but I did not spill any paint.

_____   _____

- - - - - - - - - - - - - - - -   - - - - - - - - - - - - - - - - - - -

_____   _____

- - - - - - - - - - - - - - - -   - - - - - - - - - - - - - - - - - - -

_____   _____

- - - - - - - - - - - - - - - -   - - - - - - - - - - - - - - - - - - -

Name _____

Look for mistakes with adjectives that compare.
Look for mistakes with capital letters and end marks.

Write <u>X</u> if a sentence
has any mistakes.

Write <u>C</u> if a sentence
is correct.

1. what makes the sticks fly up _____

2. You have to roll and push. _____

3. Which <u>of the three</u> sticks will spin for the long time

   of all? _____

4. Ruby's stick makes a soft sound <u>than</u> mine does. _____

5. Catch the stick before it drops! _____

6. my stick has a wider top than yours _____

© Macmillan/McGraw-Hill

**A. Circle the adjectives that compare in the sentences.
Write 2 if the adjective compares two.
Write 3 if the adjective compares three or more.**

1. Lee has the newest bike of all. _____

2. The lighter bike belongs to Pam. _____

3. This bus is bigger than that bus. _____

4. The oldest boat broke down. _____

5. The smallest plane landed first. _____

6. Which of those trains is longer? _____

7. The fastest sled dog leads the pack. _____

**B. Talk with a partner about things in your
classroom. Use adjectives that compare two
and adjectives that compare three or more.**

Name _____

Words that have the same or almost the same meaning are called **synonyms**.

Synonyms:	smile	grin
	shine	glow

Words that have opposite meanings are called **antonyms**.

Antonyms:	new	old
	up	down

Read each row of words.

Circle the two words that are synonyms.

1. kind   happen   nice   ground

2. tiny   plant   big   little

3. happy   glad   mean   grow

Circle the two words that are antonyms.

4. dig   before   after   from

5. all   seeds   nothing   green

6. wet   care   again   dry

Find the word in the second sentence that means the same as the underlined word. Write both words on the lines.

1. Mom told me to put on my <u>hat</u>.

   This cap will block the sun.

   _____

   -

   _____

2. My <u>job</u> is to dig up the dirt.

   It is hard work.

   _____

   -

   _____

Find the word that means the opposite of the underlined word. Write both words.

3. We got an <u>early</u> start.

   We worked until it was late.

   _____

   -

   _____

4. Look at how <u>big</u> the plant has grown.

   It came from such a little seed.

   _____

   -

   _____